Catch

National Literacy Strategy

Encourage your child to recognize these essential words
as you read this story:

**but   can   cat   come   jump
man   on   red   the**

Robber Red can run.

Jumping Jim can jump.

The Hat Man can hop.

Yo-yo Man can yell.

Zig Zag Zebra can zip.

Kicking King can kick!

But Clever Cat can catch!

Seven eggs

Lyn Wendon

National Literacy Strategy
Encourage your child to recognize these essential words
as you read this story:

a   an   can   had   have   I   look   no
on   red   said   seven   the

Eddy Elephant met a red hen.

The red hen had seven eggs!

"Can I have an egg?" said Eddy.

"No, no, no!" said the red hen.

"Well, well, well!" said Eddy.

What is it?

Judy Borthwick

National Literacy Strategy
Encourage your child to recognize these essential words
as you read this story:

a   and   are   at   big   cat   dog   in
is   it   little   look   no   what

Tess and Lucy are in a tent.

"Look!" says Lucy.

"Is it a bat?" says Tess.

"No, look at its legs," says Lucy.

"Is it a big dog?" says Tess.

"No," said Lucy. "It's a cat and ...

… a little kitten!"

The big fish

Sheila Blackburn

National Literacy Strategy
Encourage your child to recognize these essential words
as you read this story:

a   big   but   got   had   he   his   in   is
off   said   that   then   this   to   went

Fred went off to fish.

"This is fun!" said Fred.

Is that a fish?

Fred had to grab his net.

Then Fred fell in!

Fred got wet, but …

... he got a big fish!